WATER, WATER E

THE DRAINING O1

Trevor Be...

Ψ

PEOPLE visit the Fens to see vastness of landscape, great churches, historic towns, and marvel at famous Washland in wintertime teeming with wildfowl. It is easy to derive inspiration from acres of brown, black, gold and green, the rapier rivers, sunrise and sunset and canopy of changing sky from horizon to horizon that no other area gives. Ruggedness and independence are hallmarks of the Fens enriched with history which set these islands on a new course. Always a land of challenge the Fens have more dykes, drains and rivers than any other described area in Britain. Here is the country's very own Holland, wrested from lake and marsh by foreigners and turned into prolific agricultural and horticultural land by English and Walloon farmers. The draining of the Fens was an undertaking seldom equalled; of great courage and fraught with difficulty, loss and disappointment. A story told in the past two hundred years in great detail and at great length at prohibitive expense. In this modest work the writer endeavours to present the story to Fen inhabitants and visitors alike in concise manner, as up-to-date as possible with minimum recourse to monotonous statistics which so often accompanies great works by experts. It has been a labour of love and he hopes it will inspire pride among Fen-bred people in particular, treading in firm footsteps of their forebears who with prodigious labour achieved so much for their descendants with little reward to themselves.

ISBN 0 901680 46 1   Copyright T. Bevis 1992

Published by Trevor Bevis, BA.,28 St. Peter's Road, March, Cambs. PE15 9NA
Telephone: (01354) 657286
Printed by David J. Richards, Printers and Stationers, 1 West Park Street, Chatteris, Cambs. PE16 6AH.
Telephone: 01354 692947   Fax: 01354 692299

"Go on, Brave Undertakers and succeed
In spite of brutish clamour, take no heed
To those that curse your generous labours; he
That good refrains, cause men unthankful be."

Statistics for this book derived from:

THE GREAT LEVEL (Dorothy Summers) David & Charles 1976
by kind permission of the Publishers

A HISTORY OF THE BEDFORD LEVEL (two volumes)
Samuel Wells 1830

FENLAND NOTES & QUERIES (Ed. Rev. W. D. Sweeney, M.A.)
1900–1908

DRAINAGE OF THE MIDDLE LEVEL
(Leaflet: Middle Level Commissioners)

The author gratefully acknowledges the help of the following:
The Middle Level Commissioners at March
and, in connection with that office, Geoffrey Cave and
Russell Wright;
The Stretham Engine Trust;
Prickwillow Drainage Engine Museum Trust;
John Moore, Station Engineer and staff at Wiggenhall St. Germans

Three generations at Lakenheath: Old Lode wind engine; steam pumping station (c. 1844); and asbestos building housing a diesel pump unit.
(*Drawn from a photograph*)

An open view
of an early
Fen wind
engine

T. Bevis.

Some of the earliest wind-engines in the Fens, similar to that illustrated, were erected in the parish of Elm. (Based on W. Blith's "The English Improver Improved" (1652).

CHAPTER ONE

Men versus water

MANY titles describe the Fens. Flattened by glacial action thousands of years ago the Fens have been called The Holy Land of the English, Land of Goshen, The Nation's Breadbasket, Land of the Three-quarter Sky, and Sunset/Sunrise Country. All with good reason. Richly embellished by nature in all her dramatic, colourful moods and made prolific by the skills of men, these unrolling acres became a challenge in more senses than one. For at least seven centuries men confronted nature in attempts to reclaim drowned land and bitterness and despair heaped upon them time and time again. They toiled in an environment favoured by gnats, exquisitely suited to fish, wildfowl, osier and reed and by sheer grit eked out a living.

The notion of draining such a vast, low-lying level was deemed an incredulous thing. It was entertained for centuries but knowledge was restricted and machines yet to be invented. Three-hundred-and-fifty years ago drainage was seen as an impossible undertaking. When at last the idea was put into practice and seen to work men acknowledged the achievement as one of the wonders of the world.

A malarial morass for at least a thousand years the Fens probably adapted to a watery wilderness more by accident than natural design. Prior to 500 A.D. the level seems to have been fairly well afforested, hundreds of fossilised relics of oak, ash and pine being dragged to the surface during ploughing operations. The level was certainly higher than now. Flooding was not so much a problem as in the coastal region where Roman engineers raised sea banks and maintained the river outfalls. Traces of these great sea barriers still exist in the Marshland areas of Norfolk and Lincolnshire. Rivers carried water from the highland regions along primeval courses and farmers living on the plain were reasonably secure at their occupation.

The scene was set for a considerable disaster after the decline of Rome, and her legions and administrators recalled. From about 400 A.D. the British were left to conduct their own affairs and it is generally assumed as a consequence the vital sea defences eroded through lack of maintenance. The sea breached the embankments and water spilled into salt marshes at the rear. This would have a deteriorating effect upon the river outfalls which silted badly and the upland water no longer had unimpeded access to the sea. There was

1

only one place for it to go. It poured onto the marsh and spread from river to river reducing still further the efficiency of the outfalls. Eventually the whole plateau became a great basin, a watershed hemmed in by higher ground. Rivers pursued circuitous courses through the marsh and a change of environment transpired.

Above the watery waste protruded an archipelago of small and large islands formed of clay and of varying height. Surrounded by natural moats these islands afforded excellent sites for Anglo-Saxon settlements, tribes of soldiers-cum-farmers adapting the top soil and building enclosures for livestock. They enjoyed the benefits, too, of the Fens' natural produce of fish and wildfowl as well as harvesting bountiful crops of reed suitable for construction purposes. Island clay was conveniently obtained and used with cattle dung to build walls and timber for framework taken from well afforested commons.

The Fen islands, particularly the smallest ones, attracted hermits, recluse Christian individuals. They established cells which later became the sites of monasteries, profound halls of learning, patronised by pilgrims, kings and princes from far and near. Abbots and bishops obtained vast tracts of marsh, usually without payment in return for educating the sons and daughters of noblemen. They set up fisheries in the marsh and on the rivers and meres. Herds of cattle grazed contentedly on acquired pastures. The Fen economy benefitted considerably from the business interests of the Church and the monks were the first to explore the means of adding more to productive estates by experimenting with limited and simplified drainage. This was done on a localised scale, the Church never aspiring to an extensive system of drainage with the exception of Bishop Morton's scheme implemented near Whittlesey in the late 15th century.

As early as the 13th century, William of Malmesbury, monk and historian, wrote of his admiration for the Benedictine monks of Thorney who had successfully drained part of their extensive estate and "created a paradise" within the marsh, producing bountiful crops of all kinds and in particular fine vines to delight the palate and the eye. To achieve such acclaim the monks succeeded in bringing into production wet land situated fractionally above marsh level. They cut dykes and probably linked them to a catchwater drain where the contents found its way into the fen. In summer the system worked well. Similar systems were devised at other monasteries in the region. At Brahamwere near Ely, a small, independent monastery, the monks achieved lucrative results supported by a small harbour at the end of a drain linked to the River Ouse by which means they enjoyed good business on the waterside at Ely. Monks regularly used the rivers and meres for communication between the several monasteries which had been established in the Fens.

Independent "Courts of Sewers" existed in the 15th and 16th centuries their prime task to deepen, widen and maintain existing waterways, mainly primaeval rivers and a few artificial drains. The rivers silted badly and some were little more than long, stagnant courses their ineffectiveness causing serious floods. Regular attempts were made to improve the rivers by scouring. In 1549 the Great Ee running through March, being particularly sluggish came under supervision and orders made "that the water may be conveyed into the North Sea by the town of Wisbeche in manner and form aforetime used". Considerable maintenance work was carried out to many rivers and leams including that at Elm, the parish severely affected by severe floods on more than one occasion to the despair of inhabitants and farmers in the area. There was some improvement here and there in the Fens but on a general basis motives and methods were not always of sound reasoning and problems magnified. At Elm one or two of the first wind engines (like windmills but with a water scoop) were set up to aleviate threat of floods. These engines were invented by a Dutchman and were the inaugurators of hundreds of similar machines which were to assist in the drainage of the Fens a hundred years or so later.

The engines were erected beside dykes and drains. A notable instance was the cutting in 1568 of the Maud Foster drain and erection of an outfall sluice in Lincolnshire. This and similar schemes were designed to effect improvement on a limited basis and many were with drawbacks, the silting of outfalls setting back creditable ideas and causing promoters financial crisis. Silting of the outfalls was a hazard which no-one knew how to tackle and would not be mastered for a period of more than two hundred years.

There are numerous references to "scouring of the river at Wisbeche" which was known to change its course frequently and was particularly notorious for silting. Reference was made of the ineffectiveness of rivers in the Isle of Ely, all of which were in need of "speedy skowring". At Over, Cambs., in 1575 "in one moiste somer and an hard wynter following they loste more by death and drowning of cattell than they gained by the fennes in three years". This was a devastating period for the Fens and adjoining Marshland, a large number of inhabitants and livestock being drowned by major inflows of freshwater and sea. The first three months of the year proved disastrous with large rainfalls in February. Spring tides raised the water higher than usual and the rivers, already receiving copious amounts of fresh water burst their banks and spilled the contents far and wide. In the Marshland the situation was frightful, sea water pounding the barriers relentlessly at the behest of gales and driving ships overland. A record has it that on one occasion in the 16th century a sailing ship was thrown onto the roof of a house and the sailors lowered themselves into an upper chamber and rescued a woman about to give birth. Fierce surges resulted along the tidal rivers and damaged drains unprotected by sluices. Unable to get away the water encroached upon the land with dire consequences.

These were the years of deliberation. Men thought about the problems and attempted to tackle them on a very limited, localised scale. Year after year the "drownings" occurred with sickening frequency. Wisbech was inundated on many occasions as were the Marshland villages and Elm not only had to contend with sea flooding but received more than its share of fresh water, too. Year after year crops and livestock were devastated and the impoverished fen people "likely to be overthrown and utterly undone". People reacted with sound intentions to minimise risk of floods but often more harm than good resulted. Almost as many errors were committed as there were operations and the cost of those desperate undertakings proved to be "a tempest".

One or two medieval intellectuals had the courage to attempt major works on a big scale. In the late 13th century a Bishop of Ely caused a major cut to be made between the River Ouse near Littleport and the Wash at King's Lynn. The idea was to facilitate the speedy evacuation of water past Ely in a direct line to the sea, but the original course of the Ouse near Wisbech had insufficient flow and seriously declined. From that time the port suffered setbacks and excessive silting.

Another improver was Bishop Morton, later Cardinal and Archbishop of Canterbury. When at Ely he divided his time between ecclesiastical matters and the problems affecting the northern area of his diocese. He occasionally stayed at the castle-cum-palace at Wisbech and was able to see at first hand the devastating effect of floods in the district. The bishop was especially concerned about the deterioration of the river at Wisbech and the effect on commerce at the port through silting. Frequently ships of heavy burthen were unable to dock. The prelate-engineer came to the conclusion that he would devise a scheme with a double remedy. It involved the cutting of the leam between Stanground and Ring's End to improve drainage in the area. This was a most ambitious scheme for the drainage of the fen district in the north-west of the Isle of Ely.

Arthur Smiles in his work "Lives of the Engineers" wrote: *"The Bishop was the first to introduce into the district the practice of making straight cuts and artificial rivers for the purpose of more rapidly voiding the waters of the Fens - a practice which has been extensively adopted by the engineers of the present day."*

Commissioner for the then existing drainage authority, Bishop Morton visualised the new leam as an aid to the inflow and outflow of Wisbech river and it was carried out entirely at his own considerable expense. He made a cut forty feet wide and four feet deep named after him. From Guyhirn he continued the leam towards Wisbech and, devising additional shorter cuts he created a new outfall into the sea. Apparently the bishop attempted other drainage works but the disastrous war between the Houses of York and Lancaster prevented completion of those projects.

The area between Peterborough and Guyhirn suffered appallingly through bad drainage. Murrow bank was frequently breached by fresh water and floods wreaked considerable damage to the lands of Parson Drove, Murrow, Wisbech St. Mary, Newton and Leverington. Breaches occurred in the bank near Tydd Gote and added to the problems. Much of the fresh water came from around Thorney and it spread to such an extent it even affected Wansford far to the west. The old course of the River Nene flowing through March was navigable only in winter when water soaked the area north west of the river. During the summer March river was of no commercial value whatsoever, it being far too shallow. An alternative way for boats was via Cnut's Dyke supposedly marked out by the King's men after an hazardous journey across the fen from Ramsey to Peterborough in the 10th century. At times this ancient waterway, too, was unusable and barges from Peterborough and King's Lynn might be held up for weeks on the meres while waiting for rain and onrush of water from higher ground to swell Fen rivers.

Bishop Morton erected a building known as Tower House at Ring's End. From there he was able to supervise from an advantageous height the cutting of the leam. It was said he created a lagoon at Guyhirn for the purpose of collecting water from the leam when the Wisbech river ran at high tide. When the tide ebbed the discharge from the lagoon, backed up by water held back in the leam and along the narrow channel of Stanground chare effectively scoured the river at Wisbech forcing obstructive silt towards the outfall. The main function of Morton's Leam was to drain water from outlying land and render it less susceptible to floods. Rules entered in the Town Book of Wisbech state that the men of Wisbech Hundred were expected to scour, huff and clean the new leam all the way from the town to Midfen Tree near Whittlesey. Much animosity existed between the two towns over this arrangement, each side enthusiastically finding fault with the other!

As with all medieval drainage attempts Morton's Leam was hardly a success. For one thing it was insufficiently deep. It lacked embankments and in winter the water spilled over the land and caused serious flooding beyond an extensive area of fen as far away as March. Whittlesey farmers took advantage of the leam's meagre depth and placed gravel on its bed to facilitate easier crossing, which impeded the flow.

Nowadays the leam serves a useful purpose and commemorates an ecclesiastic of vision and integrity. Bishop Morton was the principal means of uniting the warring factions of York and Lancaster. It was written that he was a man of rare capacity and prodigious memory "which he retained and so dying still strong and full of powers."

Problems of repetitional flooding in the Fens in the 16th century were constantly before the drainage authorities, instances of which are evidenced in a report compiled by the Inquisition held by the Court of Sewers assembled at Ely in 1563:

"We ffind yt the water courses are mayntayned and kept according to the order kept at the Quene's graces court and leet in the same town (Whittlesey) the wch order is yt the stremes be in widnes xvi foot and every meer be xx widnes at the least.

"Item we ffind yt south lake is not sufficiently haffed, roked and mayntayned.

"Also we ffind yt Eldnernall Calsye (causeway) is decayed and broken down wch the water by the means whereof the water is tourned from his right course to the hyndrance of the countrie."

The expense of maintaining rivers, dykes, bridges and embankments had financial implications affecting everyone living in the Fens. Each parish had to contribute towards the upkeep of these things. For instance in the latter half of the 16th century the causeway at March was a constant source of inconvenience and the churchwardens were often approached by the town surveyor for amounts concerning his expenses and keeping the causeway in good repair. It was not unusual for parishioners to leave bequests for the maintenance of the causeway. March shared a common problem with other Fen parishes, being obliged to maintain a section of Aldreth causeway, a principal entrance into the Isle of Ely. In addition, March had to keep the bridge crossing the West Water in serviceable condition, a heavy burden upon the little town. Causeways and bridges were a vexation to the fen people, the environment creating great havoc upon essential means of communication.

The 16th century was one of trial and error. There was no clear idea as to how drainage schemes would work and how properly to apply them. There were too many individual schemes and little co-operation between their administrators. The overall body, the Court of Sewers manufactured criticism but often as not no-one took any notice. A vague idea of the shape of things to come had started to emerge. The notion of a full-scale project to drain the entire area of almost 100,000 acres of fen was no longer considered to be a fallacy. Compounded errors by abbots, bishops, farmers and noblemen had written a challenge to the future. In 1600 this manifested in the passing of an Act for the recovery of many thousand acres of marsh and other grounds within the Isle of Ely and in the counties of Cambridgeshire, Northampton, Lincoln, Norfolk, Suffolk and other counties in England.

Fen Slodgers

Where ducks by scores travers'd the Fens, coots, didappears, rails, water hens
Combined with eggs to charge our pot. Two furlongs circle round the spot.
Fowl, fish, all kinds the table grac'd; all caught within the self same space.
As time revolved, in season fed; the surplus found us salt and bread.
Your humble servant now your penman, liv'd thus, a simple, full-bred Fenman.
(Fen-Bill Hall, b. 1748).

The Old Fen (Wicken).

CHAPTER TWO

"Impossible" scheme

CREDIT for the mammoth scheme to entirely drain the Fens, a task which many believed to be impossible, falls to the genius of the eminent Dutch engineer, Sir Cornelius Veymuyden, supported by the Earl of Bedford and the intrepid Gentlemen Adventurers most of whom were previously engaged as "Participants" in the smaller but no less hazardous scheme involving Hatfield Chase in South Yorkshire. Many of the Adventurers were of foreign extract with capital. Refugees of religious intolerance they pursued the Protestant faith with sound working principles, the hallmark of Huguenots and Walloons that emigrated to England in thousands. Settling at Hatfield Chase in about 1636 the colonists were subjected to the fury of Fenmen whose livelihood of wildfowling and fishing was threatened by the scheme to produce productive land from the wastes of watery fen. On numerous occasions the English rose against the Participants, setting fire to their homes and church, breaking down sluices and destroying crops.

Vermuyden had already drawn up a plan for draining the Isle of Ely and outlying areas, and it is thought that he invited the embattled Participants to resettle in that constituency and help with the new task. Many were glad of the opportunity and some settled in the Isle in the 1640's. The colony at Thorney was finally established in 1654. The King was impressed by the Participants' achievements in Hatfield Chase, albeit under the severest difficulties. With the Earl of Bedford he visualised the Fens as a potential agricultural plain. The Earl's ambition was to eliminate the meres and drain away water through existing natural rivers and made-made dykes and drains discharging into the outfalls. Rewards, he envisaged, would be incalculable both in crop production and financially.

The Earl of Bedford, Vermuyden and 14 Gentlemen Adventurers promoted a scheme considered by many in Europe to be a waste of time and energy. Sanction was given by Parliament for the work to commence, 95,000 acres of fen allotted as recompense. The King was to receive 12,000 acres and 43,000 acres set out to provide for maintenance. The remainder would be allotted to individuals who had invested capital in the the project. None could foresee the immense problems which would arise from the undertaking.

What of the man who presented the scheme of such an ambitious undertaking? An engineer of impressive capabilty, Vermuyden had undertaken in 1626 the task of repairing the Thames banks at Dagenham. Out of recognition of his services he received a knighthood, and Royal approval was given to the scheme for draining Hatfield Chase and this was entrusted to Vermuyden.

The engineer has been described as a heavy-handed adventurer, a man with vision but lacking in finesse in the practical prosecution of his schemes and he suffered denunciation in "his misrepresentation, his system, his methods and his numerous failures." It will be seen in other pages that Vermuyden did, in fact, lack some degree of foresight but he was a victim of bitterness and jealousy. Andrew Bullard, gentleman, published a pamphlet which declared that "Sir Cornelius hath abused the King's Majesty and many of his loving subjects" in certain works in the engineer's grand scheme. "The labourers were making weak banks; making hollow and counterfeit banks of light low hassocks and sedge, skimming and destroying three times as much ground as would have performed the service if he had taken the best of the soil." He was accused of making sluices of rotten timber, mis-spending the King's treasure, undervaluing the work of the Earl of Bedford and his fellow adventurers and hindering their works as well as taking lands illegally without satisfaction.

Some of these insinuations may have been pure fabrication. Sir Cornelius did make errors of judgement, but no-one can clearly foresee the ultimate result of grandiose schemes, not even in our own times. It took over two hundred years to realise the complete drainage of the Fens. Long after Vermuyden had died a number of additions and amendments were made to the original plans. The Fens as we know them, the rivers and sluices, the sheer magnitude of the project still speak volumes for the integrity of the man, working at a time when innovations of that nature were considered to be impossible, mad ideas.

The engineer had no first-hand experience of the hostile attitudes directed against the Participants at Hatfield Chase, he then being involved with the proposed scheme of draining the Cambridgeshire Fens. His last transaction at Hatfield Chase concerned conveyance of land in 1654, the same year in which the Huguenot/Walloon colony at Thorney was formed.

Key to Vermuyden's plan lay between Earith in the old county of Huntingdonshire and Denver in Norfolk, a distance of approximately 21 miles. Between these two places he caused a 70 ft wide cut to be excavated across the Black Fens. This acted as a bypass for the River Great Ouse which skirted Ely and the West Water with a circuitous course towards Ramsey. On this new cut depended to a large extent the success of his general scheme which was not so much to guarantee the Fens remain entirely dry throughout the winter months, but in accordance with the Earl of Bedford's desire to allow farmers to use the land during the spring, summer and autumn cycles. Vermuyden could not guarantee that the Fens would be free of some inundation in the winter, a hesitancy on his part which earned him undue criticism. The farming fraternity probably expected too much from the scheme and the work entailed, believing that everything would be perfect from the word go. That, however, was not to be the case.

Caution was thrown to the winds as the new drained lands were occupied. When the winter snow and rain had saturated the ground, rendering it unworkable, Veymuyden and the Adventurers faced scathing objections accompanied by degrees of violence in the few years preceding the Civil War. The disputes had a hearing at an appropriate Court held at St. Ives and the drainage undertaking was adjudged complete. Voices were raised against the decision, proclaiming that the work was nowhere like being complete and that what had been done was virtually ineffective. Later the findings at St. Ives were declared invalid and the Adventurers faced bankruptcy.

Charles the First projected himself as the scheme's saviour and declared that he would finish what the Adventurers had failed to do. But there were strings attached to his proposition. The King himself was periously near to bankruptcy and he visualised a revised scheme from which he would emerge in a sound financial position. As his share of the reward he would take 47,000 acres, but his wild excess of spending would be unimpaired, the monarch even making plans to build a luxurious palace on a site at Manea in the middle of the royal estate. The King retained Vermuyden as chief engineer and the latter prepared a revised report with recommendations for a new scheme. The second scheme is identifiable with the layout of the present system of drainage and may be compared with the first plan shown elsewhere in this book.

As is the usual tendency in men's intentions fate took a hand in the proceedings. The King's position was becoming progressively insecure and with the outbreak of Civil War smouldering unrest in the Fens accelerated. Oliver Cromwell, himself a man of the Fens, was a member of a group which disapproved of the scheme to drain the wetlands principally because of the King's capitalist interest in the scheme by which he intended to possess thousands of acres of reclaimed land. Cromwell did not himself disapprove of the idea in general and at the end of the Civil War, the King being dead, he gave approval to the scheme. Initially Cromwell inspired confidence among the inhabitants, that their despair at losing the meres would turn to joy and prosperity from the rich crops to be grown there.

Francis Earl of Bedford died and was succeeded by his heir, William. Cornelius Vermuyden, no longer working to conditions imposed by the ill-fated King began a new scheme and another group of Adventurers was formed to implement a new Act of Parliament which decreed that the Fens be entirely drained, the system to be controllable in winter as well as in summer so that rape, coleseed, corn, hemp and flax could suitably mature and be harvested without hindrance at the appropriate times.

However, the Fenmen had second thoughts and objected to the work in any form, viewing it not without justification as interferring with their birthright and livelihood. The Gentlemen Adventurers, mindful of the Participants' experiences at Hatfield Chase, were still uneasy. Vurmuyden was as unpopular as ever and every effort was made by objectors to undermine the scheme. The Fen people were a hardy, independent breed and highly suspicious of and seldom tolerable to strangers. Vermuyden was a foreigner, the chief enemy, the author of a project which for reasons of their livelihood they would not and could not approve. If the scheme succeeded greater taxation would be heaped upon them and they were right in their views that dire poverty would descend to their feet. As it turned out four or five generations suffered from depressed economy in the area, the result of error and lack of foresight.

The first (Old Bedford) river was already working and a great barrier bank raised in the close proximity of higher ground in Huntingdonshire. A second river (New Bedford or Hundred Foot) was cut parallel to the first from Earith to Denver and embanked. The banks of the Old Bedford river were raised and the pastures between the two great waterways set out as washland acting as a safety valve in the event of abnormally wet seasons. Sluices were erected to control water and bar the tide along the River Ouse south of Denver. The plan allowed for the release of water from the two artificial waterways into the River Ouse at ebb tides to scour the river north of Denver. Fenland was divided into separate Levels. Land south-east of the Old and New Bedford rivers was recognised as the

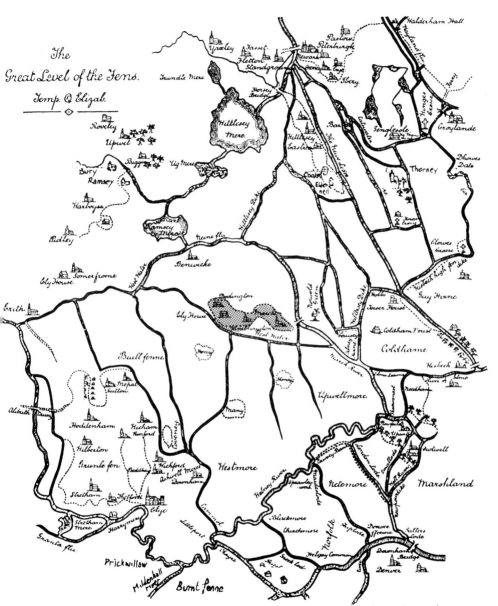

A map of the Fenland river system drawn during the reign of Queen Elizabeth the First, showing the meres and primeval waterways.

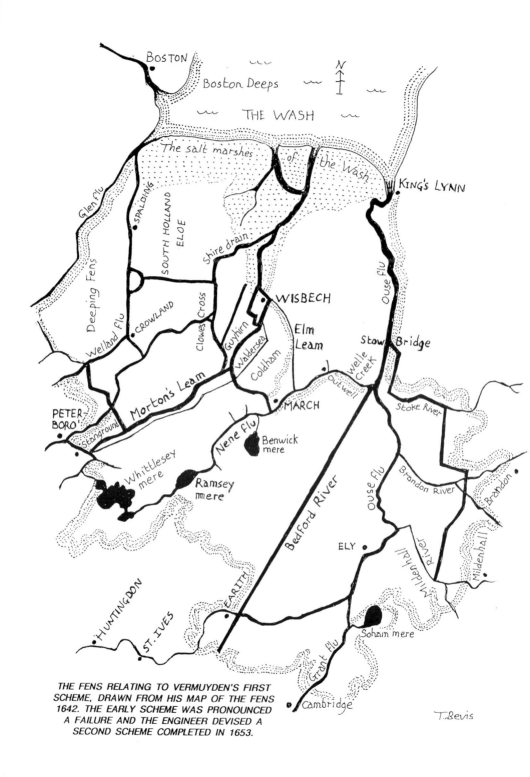

BOSTON

Boston Deeps

N

THE WASH

The salt marshes of the Wash

KING'S LYNN

Glen Flu

SPALDING

SOUTH HOLLAND ELOE

Shire drain

Deeping Fens

Welland Flu

CROWLAND

Clowes Cross

Guyhirn

Waldersea

WISBECH

Elm Leam

Ouse Flu

Stow Bridge

Coldham

Welle Creek

Stoke River

PETER-BORO'

Stanground

Morton's Leam

Outwell

MARCH

Nene Flu

Benwick mere

Whittlesey mere

Ramsey mere

Bedford River

Ouse Flu

Brandon River

Brandon

Mildenhall River

ELY

EARITH

HUNTINGDON

ST. IVES

Grant Flu

Soham mere

Mildenhall

Cambridge

THE FENS RELATING TO VERMUYDEN'S FIRST
SCHEME, DRAWN FROM HIS MAP OF THE FENS
1642. THE EARLY SCHEME WAS PRONOUNCED
A FAILURE AND THE ENGINEER DEVISED A
SECOND SCHEME COMPLETED IN 1653.

T.Bevis

Wind Engines

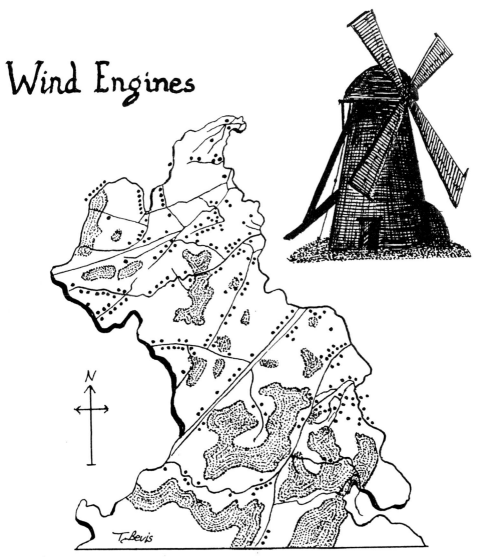

Wind engines located within the Isle of Ely, from a Map of the County of Cambridge and Isle of Ely (R. G. Baker, 1812). The Isle had about 230 wind-driven devices which were none too reliable, often becalmed and prone to storm damage. They were eventually replaced by 19 steam pumps. Shaded areas represent fen islands and upland.

Water pumps abounded near March..
After a painting of derelict pump, 1861.

"Wherever engines are necessary to facilitate a drainage, I recommend the steam-engine, to accompany the wind-engines in a considerable work; because it too frequently happens that a calm succeeds an abundant fall of rain for a considerable length of time." (T. Stone, AGRICULTURE OF THE COUNTY OF LINCOLN, 1794).

South Level; the Middle Level, the largest drainage area, forms a triangle between Earith, Wiggenhall St. Germans and Peterborough; and the North Level covers the remainder.

While the artificial rivers were being created it was necessary to cut numerus dykes across the levels and link them directly and indirectly to the main drains. People living in the Fens are literally surrounded by a network of dykes and drains which slice through the land as straight as the proverbial arrow. After an existence of more than 350 years Vermuyden's framework of drains still function. They are called leams, eaus and on old maps some are "flu's" derived from confluence which means a place where rivers join. Fen people usually call them "cuts" and "drains." Most are named after varying widths from the ridges of banks and are wider than they were originally. Old and not so old and re-cut from time to time they materialised over a period of 500 years, the oldest, Morton's Leam in 1478-90, and the latest the new Catchwater Drain near Bevill's Leam in 1983. The majority date from the 17th century (approximate): Popham's Eau 1605, Peakirk Drain 1631, Horseshoe Sluice 1631, New South Eau 1631, Bevill's Leam 1631, Sam's Cut 1631, and Old Bedford River 1631. Most of these drains date from Vermuyden's first scheme. The second scheme comprised the New Bedford River (Hundred Foot) 1651, Sixteen Foot Drain 1651, Twenty Foot River (Moore's Drain) 1651, Forty Foot River (Vermuyden's Drain) 1651, and Tong's Drain 1653. Waterways are controlled by a system of sluices and manned and automatic pumps discharge into them from feeder dykes.

Numerous improvements were carried out to the general drainage in later years. The River Nene between Wisbech and Peterborough was cut in 1728 and named Smith's Leam. The remainder of the river from Wisbech to its outfall at Sutton Bridge was recut three times. The present course replaces a notorious, circuitous waterway which had a tendency to change direction (see plan). The Ouse Cut materialised in 1827, a considerable improvement on the old waterway. The North Level Main Drain was made in 1831-4, and the Middle Level Main Drain in 1848. A number of natural rivers - The Nene (old course), Whittlesey Dyke. Catwater, Old South Eau, Great River Ouse, West Water, Little Ouse River, River Lark, River Cam and the River Welland - are linked directly and indirectly to the system. In the 17th century when the first and second drainage schemes were implemented the Fens generally lay at a higher level than today and the labyrinth of dykes discharged into artificial drains by reason of the area's natural gradient, but that would change.

CHAPTER THREE

Rebellious Fenmen

WITH difficulty the huge task proceeded towards its doubtful conclusion. Obtaining labourers proved to be a problem. Vexed over the changes which threatened them, Fenmen flatly refused to help in any way and at every opportunity sallied forth at night to breach the banks and set fire to sluices. From the times it had been rumoured that designs were afoot to change their environment and foreigners set loose in the marsh "the inhabitants, aghast at the idea, vehemently objected through printed matter." When the spade made the first cut onto the wet land the Fenmen rose up in all their fury and did all they could to hinder operations. One, Richard Atkins of Outwell, determined "to try the fennes with an augur, 11 feet long with which he did his best to render useless the dykes and drains." Men in the Isle of Ely regularly breached the banks, often at their families' risk, and people were "drowned in beds within their houses." Some actions were seen as criminal acts as that when vandals directed violence against the Podyke, subjecting the new bank to great damage, water pouring from it ruining the land around.

There was also cash flow problems and work proceeded at an intolerably slow pace. At the time the country was embroiled in Civil War and this, too, hindered work. The stagnant nature of the undertaking came before Parliament and the government, concerned at the expense of keeping thousands of prisoners-of-war decided that hundreds of men be brought to the Fens. (More of that on another page). When eventually in 1653 the initial task had been completed a service of thanksgiving was held in Ely cathedral. There, experts, principal citizens and farmers gahered in the nave of the majestic church which looks appropriately across the limitless reaches of black fen, no longer the domain of water but nurtured into fruitful production. The congregation visualised a local economy beyond all imagination, but no-one had an inkling of the disasters which would befall the Fens over the following two hundred years, trying men to the point of insolvency.

Vermuyden, then a naturalised Englishman basking in the glow of achievement, might have been forgiven in later years if he had wished he had never been involved. Unknown to the farmers the project was only partly successful. It was necessary to inaugurate a system of maintaining the rivers, sluices and embankments and to that end the Bedford Level Corporation was formed. Large tracts of former wet fen were allotted to the Adventurers who set about preparing the land for intensive farming.

For a time all went well, then the bombshell dropped. It was soon obvious that foresight had fallen short among the engineers who had not allowed for land shrinkage and, to worsen matters harbour authorities, such as at King's Lynn, began complaining of silting in the rivers causing hazards to ships leaving and entering port. The latter problem had been thought possible and to counteract it Vermuyden erected a sluice at Denver to restrict the water to one channel. However, the flow of water was weaker than anticipated and silt was deposited at each ebb tide. The River Ouse suffered through restricted flow and the river bed gradually built up. Mud from the upland regions had insufficient force to carry it and it fell to the bottom.. The effect on water-borne traffic became serious and protests heard from communities whose economies were dependent upon the river systems. Some Fenmen who had reluctantly come to terms with the decline of fisheries, and others with vested interest in the land became vociferous. The alarming situation was heightened when pressure of water along the river banks in the South Level broke the barriers and saturated the land.

The unexpected had happened. Bellringers hastened to church towers and rang the bells to warn inhabitants to collect livestock and belongings and flee to the islands or face being engulfed by the water. Calamities like that – and there were several – were not always caused by strength of nature. Star Chamber entries for the reign of Charles the First indicate that irresponsible "Fen Slodgers" had deliberately caused breaches in river banks in order to spite Vermuyden and his fellow Adventurers. The engineer had a great deal of trouble from rebellious Fenmen, especially when supervising the excavation of the Forty Foot river.

Complaints were well advertised. Dugdale, in his published work, included a local song "The Powte's Complaint," three of the verses capturing the unsalutory spirit of the times:

"Come brethren of the water and let us all assemble
To treat upon the matter which makes us quake and tremble,
For we shall rue it, if't be true that the Fens be undertaken,
And when we feed in fen and reed, they'll feed both beef and
bacon.

"They'll sow both beans and oats wherever man yet thought it,
Where men did row in boats, 'ere undertakers bought it;
But, Ceres, thou behold us now – let wild oats be their
*   venture,*
Oh! let the hogs and miry bogs destroy where they do
*   enter.*

"Away with boats and rudders; farewell both boats and
*   skatches,*
No need of one t'other, men now make better matches.
Stilt makers all and tanners shall complain of this disaster,
For they will make each muddy lake for Essex calves and
*   pasture. "*

Ψ

Vermuyden's reasoning that the flow of rivers to the outfalls is determined by volume and gradient is true. He had thought that water would pass along the length of its course, losing gradient gradually, and that it would enter into the channel influenced by strong ebb tides. This did happen for a time but the engineer failed to include the possibility of a phenomenon peculiar to these parts. As water drains from the land the peat must shrink and imperceptible depressions occur in the Fens. The water in the rivers which formerly shared the same level of the land must inevitably flow at a higher level than the countryside. Subsequently, water from the upland regions meeting winter and spring tides would exert tremendous pressure upon the river banks. This often happened along the banks of the River Nene between Tydd Gote and Wisbech, water flowing past the sluice at Dog-in-a-Doublet meeting the spring tides, then rapidly ascending the river banks. Resulting from this streets and houses near Wisbech port became flooded. Flood gates and reinforced brick walls overlooking the Nene has helped to eradicate the problem.

Various incidents were recorded of breaches occuring along the north bank of Morton's Leam which discharged into the river near Wisbech, thence into the sea. Water spread over the fen at considerable distances. In 1770, for instance, it spread out from breached banks as far as Granoke House, Sutton St. Edmund, obliging farmers to remove livestock to higher ground. A mark on a willow tree at Wryde indicated the depth of water which, in the vicinity of

Thorney stood at depths of up to six feet, forcing Daniel le Haire a local farmer to live in the upper chambers of his house. An observer working on Thorney estate wrote a graphic account of those traumatic times when people lived in fear of river banks being breached:

"Although there has been no inundation of the North Level since 1770, a breach of the bank has frequently been expected. The farmers took it by turns to watch the water when very high that there was a probability of its running over the bank. An alarm bell was ordered to be rung in case of danger to give warning to the tenantry to make their property secure. Warehouses were erected by the North Level Commissioners at convenient distances along the bank to hold the necessary tools and 'weazon' stakes which were plunged into small breaches to hold soil thrown onto them.

"On one occasion, Mr. S. Egar and his friend (the farmers watched in pairs) had a beat of about two miles long in the weakest part of the bank. Workmen were walking to and fro to be ready at call. It was night, the water rising gradually but perceptibly. The bank must go . . . but where was the weakest place? Gauges were carefully examined and revealed that the water had fallen. Their feverish anxiety knew no bounds . . . Where had it given way? They galloped off to spread the news and prepare their neighbours. The relief, said an old man years after, can be more easily imagined than described when it was found that the bank on the south side had given way – that all in Thorney were safe."

That was the situation in the Fens a hundred-and-twenty years after the completion of the drainage scheme, when the instruments of drainage were well established in the shape of sluices and wind engines, like windmills, erected at the side of drains and ditches. The engineers had entirely overlooked the significance of removing too much water from the land. It was an error that many of the embankments had been built of light soil which the water easily eroded. But in all fairness, the early years more than three centuries ago were very much the years of experiment, of trial and error, and it is understandable as to how and why things went wrong.

As the land continued to shrink more work was entailed in deepening the dykes so that fields would be more effectively drained, but in deepening them the water was not able to be discharged into the higher rivers and drains. The rivers could not be deepened and water levels remained high. It did not help that non-shrinking silt adjacent to the coastal region had the effect of barriers and with tidal assistance held the fresh water back.

16

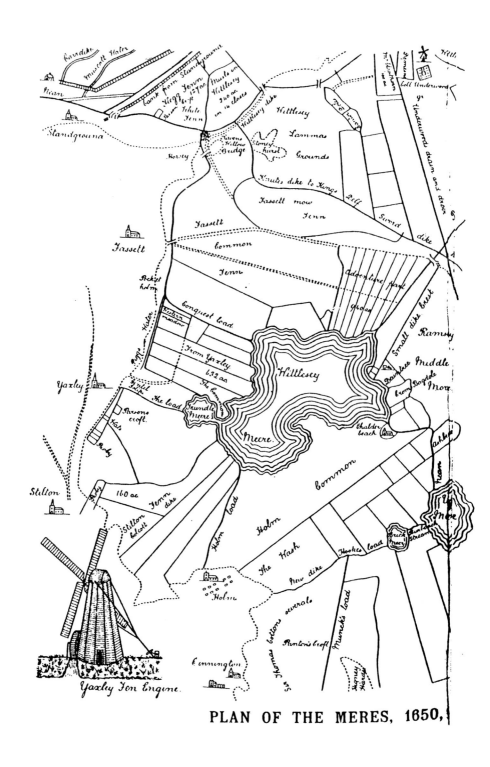

PLAN OF THE MERES, 1650,

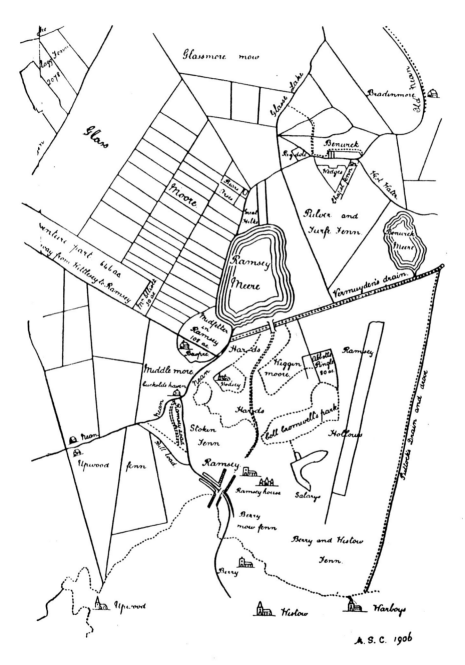

taken from Jonas Moore's Survey.

Flooding occurred in the late 17th century and throughout the 18th century, productive land disappearing beneath water to the despair of farmers. They had vacated secure homes upon the islands and lived in the reclaimed fen for convenience of farming. When river banks burst and water spread in all directions the farmers were literally helpless. All that they could do was collect their families and possessions (if they had the time) and withdraw to higher ground. To add insult to injury the farmers suffered greater taxation which was imposed by the Bedford Level Corporation who was responsible for repairing and raising the river banks which rapidly deteriorated from land shrinkage. Farmers in the Marshland area of King's Lynn, Wisbech and Spalding experienced even greater difficulties, not so much as a result of fresh water floods but incursion by the sea. In these regions flooding was on a massive scale.

Inhabitants, at Elm and Tydd for instance, had to contend with floods from both quarters. People living there had no security like their cousins in the Fens where the islands remained comparatively dry in all seasons. Buildings in the Marshland areas stood more or less on the same level as the sea. When the sea forced its way through the huge sea banks and the outfalls poured water into the salt marsh, inhabitants found themselves in a perilous situation. Lives were lost as well as homes, crops and livestock.

Many sought refuge in church towers. At Terrington St. Clement the church was frequently used in this way when buildings were threatened by the sea. *"Some went to the church, some to the haystacks, some to the baulks of houses till they were near famished; poor women leaving their children swimming in their beds 'til good people adventuring their lives went up to the breast in the water to fetch them out of the windows, whereof Mr. Brown, the minister, did fetch divers to the church on his back, and if it had not pleased God to move the hearts of the Mayor and aldermen of King's Lynn with compassion, who sent beer and victuals thither by boat, many would have perished."* People living in the areas where the silt and peat soil merged, faced appalling difficulties. Wisbech, the Waltons, Walpoles, the Terringtons and other places regularly received the unwelcome attention of salt water and fresh water incursion. In one instance in the 13th century Wisbech was awash to such extent as to devastate the formidable Norman castle.

In the seasons of rain, wind and snow the Black Fens of the Isle of Ely reverted to their original state and many of the inhabitants returned to their former livelihood - wild fowling, sedge cutting and fishing. Several farmers, exasperated by the worsening situation, re-settled on the islands, and some left the Fens. Others, putting their faith in the future set their teeth and determined to battle on. The Bedford Level Corporation had little success in instilling confidence into the farming community and was compelled to resort to a policy of trial and error. The dissatisfied farmers began taking matters into their own hands and erected scores of wind engines to discharge water from the fields. As it turned out it was an imperfect practice but a justified means on the road to resolving unforeseen problems.

Scene in Marshland during the Inundation of 1862. From a Photograph.

Benwick Wind Engine

T.A.Bevis

CHAPTER FOUR

The elegant wind engine

AS long ago as the 16th century private wind engines, much like windmills, were erected in various parts of the Fens. Such machines driven by wind power were numerous in Holland which is credited with the invention of these old-world wind-driven devices for compelling water along the dikes and lifting it into the main drains. Very elegant they looked, too, sails idling on the breeze but they were dependent on kindly elements and gales proved very destructive to many. A few were evident in the Southern Fens in about 1580, farmers at Elm employing the machines to drain land. They were simply constructed, and not as lofty as most of the engines or mills used in the 18th century. The majority of Fenland wind engines applied to land drainage only. Those erected in Holland and on the Norfolk Broads could additionally be adapted to grind corn.

The object of the wind engine is to lift water a few feet and discharge it into the drain at a higher level. It was equipped with a wheel fitted with scoops. Wind was the favoured source of power but in some parts of the world it was the custom to use manpower to drive water wheels. Oxen and horses had been used for working various shapes and sizes of water engines sited on smaller acreages, a system entirely unsuitable for the Fens. The wind engine, usually called a windmill, evolved from the mill and similar primitive machines. Over the years it became taller to gain advantage of air movement and was fitted with larger scoopwheels.

As more and more Fen farmers erected privately owned wind engines there was a danger of the drainage system such as existed becoming one with little or no co-ordination. Often as not the water they scooped damaged banks as it splashed into the drains or caused harm to another land owner. In certain cases the Bedford Level Corporation had given consent for farmers to erect their own engines but the time came when it was necessary to refuse permission and many of the towers were forcibly dismantled. A lot of controversy arose and barbed comments aimed by individuals at the Corporation seemed to have little effect. The farmers learned that the individual had practically no chance of making any progress, but where groups of people vent grievances against authorised bodies in this case the Bedford Level Corporation, officials were obliged to take note.

Fed up with repetitive "drownings" and weary of apparent inactivity to remedy the situation, farmers at Haddenham in 1726 formed their own drainage body to care for members' interests in the area between Earith and the Isle of Ely. The idea had been raised several times, the farmers having seen what the land was capable of producing in lenient seasons. Then came the wet years which convinced them that they must form their own board and take whatever action was necessary, principally to erect wind engines at strategic places on the land in Haddenham Fen. This example prompted farmers in other Fen districts to obtain Acts of Parliament and eventually the internal drainage of the Bedford Level was managed by various local boards pumping water from their designated areas into the main rivers and drains which remained in the care of the Bedford Level Corporation.

The elegant wind engines introduced a romantic and mysterious air to the Fens. More's the pity that not a single one was preserved in the Level which they prominently dominated more than two hundred years ago. What a splendid sight it must have been to look along the arrow straight course of Vermuyden's Drain (Forty Foot) and count as many as forty lined up along the banks, sails revolving idly or briskly according to the strength of the wind. The wooden towers stood 40 feet high on substantial bases and they were capped by moveable wooden heads. Timber was used in their construction as heavier materials would cause the towers to sink into the soil. Sails were 36 feet long and six or seven feet broad covered by canvas which was encased when not required. Several wind engines continued to be used well after the establishment of steam powered pumps. A few, smaller, open wind-driven devices were used in the fields after the introduction of diesel pump units in the early part of the 20th century. (See illustration of Benwick wind engine). Alas, conservationists turned away their eyes and the idling sails were abandoned to neglect or demolished in the wake of diesel efficiency.

Compared with their successors the steam powered pumps, wind engines were simple in design and operation (see exploded illustration of 17th century machine). It comprised huge beams of seasoned oak, the vertical shaft geared to sail arms on a revolving head. The lower half was attached to a system of cogwheels, and the final drive attached to an external scoopwheel, in later machines usually half encased. Depending on the size of the engine scoopwheels could be as much as 30 feet in diameter studded with wooden boards splashing into the water.

The basement usually served as living space for the attendant and his family. During the summer months he lived in a cottage and earned his living maintaining dykes. At Michaelmas they all moved into the engine tower and stayed there until the following April or May. Looking after wind engines was arduous work commencing at an early hour until late at night. This was especially true of February when consistently heavy rain threatened to drown young wheat. The attendant had always to be on hand to work the chain and windlass by which he manoeuvred the engine's upper section to present the sails to the breeze or wind; he had also to gather in the canvas should gales threaten to tear it to pieces. He was obliged to answer for damage and if he proved reckless in the management of the machinery the sails might easily snap off like a carrot. Such an error compelled his presence before irate commissioners, generally farmers who, like their labourers, knew a thing or two about the Fens.

A former rector of St. Wendreda's church, March, keenly interested in Fenland history, entered in his diary a conversation he had in 1890 with a retired engine attendant: *"You see, master, it was just like this. She (the wind engine) was going all the winter when she could, but the water all ran back again. It couldn't get away and often enough there was no wind for weeks together in the winter time. That's how the land came to be drowned. But, bless you, it's all altered now with these here steamers. Why! they can drain every drop out of the land and the rivers are always a-running."*

The graceful wind engines were constantly in need of repair. Unruly elements often ripped sails and played havoc with the structure, loosening wooden boards. On many occasions when the machines were most needed there was insufficient wind to drive them. Danger prevailed too, the sails sweeping down as little as three feet from the doorstep of the entrance. The attendant's children ran in and out quite unconcerned of the danger, yet somehow they managed to avoid the sails. Realistically, the wind engine can be credited with some degree of success in the drainage of such a large area as the Fens. They were unreliable and terribly uneconomic to maintain but there was nothing else to do the job.

To see wind engines working at their best in the late 18th century one would have to go to Holland and Flanders. The banks in those flat countries were well made of a mixture of diverse substances, whereas in the Fens light soil was often used and it all too easily eroded. The weaker parts of embankments in Holland were reinforced with timber and brickwork, ". . . but being deprived in most places of the advantage of having the land waters drained into cuts and canals by the common methods of valves or tunnels, because of the very low situation of the lands, in respect to the surface of those rivers and canals; the Hollanders keep their lands drained by the help of engines, principally windmills, well made, properly situated and their number suited to the water they are to throw out. It is common in those countries to see three or four windmills playing one to another so that the water is raised over a perpendicular bank, sometimes twelve or fourteen feet in height." This system, known as "double lift" was adopted at many places in the English Fens. A world of difference existed between the low countries of Holland and Flanders and the Fen district and failure to recognise this accounted to a large degree for the extravagant outlay and irretrievable misfortunes that occurred. It proved to experts in a later age that the adoption of principles and plans, however judicious and successful in one country, could well prove inapplicable to another.

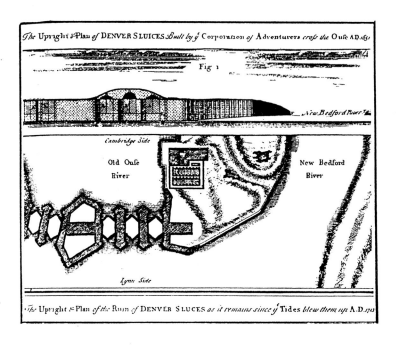

Denver Sluice built in 1651.   Collapsed 1713.
Taken from T. Badeslade, "Hist. Navig. King's Lynn" 1725.

In 1713 the sluice at Denver collapsed, much to the delight of the anti-drainage brigade who hoped by this, the Fens would revert to their former watery state. To some extent their wish was granted. The Bedford Level Corporation faced problems of the greatest magnitude – the River Ouse had narrowed, outfalls had choked with silt, banks were constantly being eroded and ships found navigational channels difficult to negotiate. Parts of the fens were always under water and it seemed that nothing would be done, or could be done to remedy it. At best the depressed fens acted as a safety valve much as the existing washlands at Welney and Whittlesey, and Fenmen took out punts and boats and returned to their old pursuits of wildfowling and fishing. Bedford Level Corporation became the whipping post for irritated farmers and ship users and the Fenmen, benefitting from the problems organised petitions against the rebuilding of Denver Sluice. Arguments went backwards and forwards for 40 years and the matter finally resolved with the rebuilding of the sluice. From the mid 18th century to 1800 more wind engines were erected by authority of the North, Middle and South Levels acting independently of each other. Each governed its affairs and had its own outfall, provided the necessary means of ridding its area of unwanted water and levied charges to enable essential work to be undertaken.

Newly drained land had great potential and it was gradually acknowledged that one day the drainage operation would wholly succeed. Some living in the Fens still regarded the whole thing as a waste of time and money. As the drained fens sank the river banks were raised higher and still serious floods occurred. Thousands of acres were waterlogged to such depths that farmers gave up the struggle and abandoned their fields.

With the dawning of the 19th century the whole question of drainage was reassessed. A new age had arrived and with it a new power, steam. A major drawback to older schemes was that the River Ouse had no direct outfall to the sea, the last few miles of its course near King's Lynn drawn out in the shape of a half moon. This restricted the flow of water and contributed to silting upstream. For many years it had been suggested that this harmful bend (see map) be by-passed to allow the water a stronger outfall. The harbour authorities at Lynn viewed the idea with suspicion and it was not until a hundred years had passed and at a cost of £12,000 in legal expenses, was it finally agreed to dig the Eau Bank Cut. Denver Sluice was again rebuilt and various modifications to the river carried out to facilitate a rapid passage of water to the sea.

In 1827 a new cut was made to facilitate improved flow of the Great Ouse River in the vicinity of Ely. This also benefitted the discharge of the River Lark and River Little Ouse. Similar improvements were made to the River Nene north of Wisbech which had a long history of navigational problems caused by sluggish movement and build-up of silt. A "New River" from Wisbech to the Wash had been cut in 1636, replacing "Wisbech Old River" a natural waterway which coursed like a serpent and made navigation in and out of Wisbech port extremely hazardous. (See Plan of Wisbech River 1636). In 1773 this section was widened and renamed Kinderley's Cut. The outfall, too, received remedial treatment in 1830 being made deeper and wider. These improvements rendered the new course of the River Nene navigable as far as Peterborough until the installation of the sluice at Dog-in-a-Doublet near Whittlesey. A long standing problem at Wisbech, a phenomenon known as the "Aegar", a combination of spring tides and strong winds often caused the river to flow over its banks and flood streets in and around the port area. As a precaution walls and floodgates were erected in the 20th century to restrict high water to its channel.

By the time the bells had welcomed 1830 and had rung at Queen Victoria's accession, the pattern of Fen dykes, rivers and drains, the sluices and hundreds of wind engines had had telling effect on the drainage of the three Levels, albeit at tremendous expense. Farms were beginning to flourish and the Fens slowly emerged from a depression of two centuries duration. Administration of the South, Middle and North Levels was confused, large numbers of local farmers sitting on the boards levying their own tax, but they were careful to act within the jurisdiction of the Bedford Level Corporation. The Corporation stood at the threshold of a new and powerful innovation – the steam engine. This was to be employed on a grand scale in the Fens. The roar of escaping steam and steady stroke of vertical pistons ushered in the new age of economy for the flatlands and realised at long last the dream of Vermuyden and his fellow Adventurers.

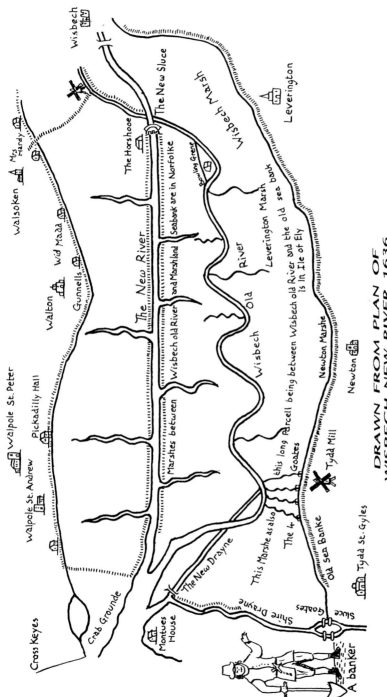

DRAWN FROM PLAN OF
WISBECH NEW RIVER 1636

The Old River's irregular course made navigation to Wisbech Port very difficult and contributed to serious silting. In 1773 a new cut was made between Wisbech and Tydd and the outfall section cut in 1830.

T. Bevis

Cross Keyes
Crab Grounde
Walpole St. Andrew
Walpole St. Peter
Pickadilly Hall
Walsoken
Walton
Wid Madd
Gunnells
Mrs Hardy
Wisbech
The Horshooe
The New River
Wisbech old River and Marshland
Seabank are in Norfolke
The New Sluce
Bowling Grene
Wisbech Marsh
Leverington
Leverington Marsh
Wisbech Old River
this long Parcell being between Wisbech old River and the old sea bank is In Ile of Ely
Marshes between
Montues House
The New Drayne
This Marshe as also
The 4 Goates
Old Sea Banke
Shire Drayne
Sluce Goates
Tydd St. Gyles
Tydd Mill
Newton Marshe
Newton
A banker

Nineteenth century improvements to the River Nene

CRAB HOLE

X 1830 CUT

SUTTON BRIDGE

X GUNTHORPE SLUICE

N. Level Main Drain

X KINDERLEY'S CUT

X WOODHOUSE MARSH CUT (Paupers' Cut)

X THE HORSESHOE

WISBECH

X RUMMER'S MILL

GUYHIRN

The River Nene outfall underwent several improvements in the 19th century. It was straightened in alignment above Kinderley's Cut between 1821 and 1832. This work was carried out at Woodhouse Marsh after which the new cut was named, but according to a Minute entered for Wisbech Corporation on December 6th 1826, it was known locally as Paupers' Cut, able-bodied men of Wisbech and surrounding district thrown on the poor rate being obliged to construct it. It provided them with work for several years.

This and other improvements to the river considerably assisted the flow and made navigation less hazardous. About 3,000 acres of marshland was reclaimed as a result of improved drainage and embankment work. At Wisbech the increased scour of the river actually lowered the river bed by almost ten feet. This resulted in increased cargo tonnage of 167,447 in 1847, compared with 55,040 in 1829 and 63,180 in 1830.

Similarly, improvements made to the river from Guyhirn to Peterborough resulted in its alignment more or less with Morton's Leam. This stretch of the Nene was given a bottom forty feet wide and forelands of fifty feet made on each side between the foot of the banks and the slopes of the cut.

CHAPTER FIVE

In fitness for the urgent hour

THE greatest industrial advance in the Victorian age was the harnessing of steam. Experiments were first conducted with steam in the 18th century and the inauguration of railway locomotives in the following century illustrated the numerous uses to which the revolutionary new power could be applied. The first steam pump was installed at Sutton St. Edmunds in about 1812. Over the following forty years steam-driven waterscoops were allocated to many places in the Fens. When travelling in the Fens one sees, here and there, remains of brick engine houses, quite devoid of machinery. Some still retain lofty chimneys from which smoke escaped from coal-stoked boilers. At least one old engine near Holme Fen worked from a diet of locally produced turves. Coal was expensive and most of it was transported along the fen river system.

The power plants which turned huge scoopwheels were known as beam engines, a shaft from the vertical cylinder rocking a huge iron overhead beam linked to a crank driving the scoopwheel. By 1851 the steam pump had become very sophisticated and one was employed for the first time to drain Whittlesey Mere in the same year. At first drainage was attempted by making a cut in the bank and water flowed freely for several days into the exterior river. "The first rush of water subsided on the second day and at the end of three weeks . . . only a very sluggish stream passed outwards." Natural drainage of the mere could not be maintained . . . "and one of Messrs. Easton and Amos's newly invented Apold pumps was erected, capable of discharging 16,000 gallons per minute with a six feet lift and worked by a 25 h.p. engine." This effort was in vain as in the following Autumn heavy rains swelled the rivers and the bank burst and "in a few hours Whittlesey Mere, southern England's largest freshwater lake, was itself again," a thousand acres covered with two-and-a-half feet of water. After three weeks of consistent pumping the Mere finally succumbed and was made as dry as any other part of the Fens.

The beam engines were much more reliable than those driven by wind, and the buildings containing them seldom prone to damage by unruly elements. They were never becalmed and would work if necessary days and weeks on end, their only requirement, fuel.

Like sentinels they waited in fitness for the urgent hour. On the road to Pymoor, opposite the lofty bank of the New Bedford River, stands a defunct engine house next to a diesel driven pump. An interesting plaque attached to the external wall bears this inscription:

> *The Fens have oft-times by water drowned,*
> *Science a remedy in WATER found;*
> *The powers of STEAM, she said, shall be employ'd,*
> *And the Destroyer by itself destroyed.*

Steam power in the form of the slow-running but inexorably powerful beam engine hastened the demise of storm prone wind engines. At their zenith in the 1750's the "windmills" of the Fens numbered about 750 but only about 250 remained when the first slim chimney appeared above the fields. Most wind engines were owned by farmers and worked relatively small areas. Many suffered damage through tempests; others were neglected and allowed to decay. The system powered by steam guaranteed all-round consistency which the wind engine could not do. Even so, for several years scaled down skeletal wind-driven waterscoops stood alongside dykes and served as secondary units coaxing water towards drains served by steam and early diesel pumps. They were much lower in height with moveable heads and sails mounted on timber and iron frames.

We that live in the southern Fens are fortunate that one of the beam engines, last worked during the Second World War, was handed down more or less intact. It is at Stretham and is cared for by the Stretham Engine Preservation Trust. This fine old engine, its lofty chimney a notable landmark in this part of the Fens, is reached by a narrow metalled lane off the road to Wicken. Basically erected in 1831 the engine and its huge scoopwheel cost £2,900 and the building to contain it £2,050. Some additions were made over the years but most of the machinery is original. From 1925 until March 11th, 1941 the engine worked 400 hours. It has since remained inactive.

It is a very impressive piece of machinery, evocative of quality and soundness of construction for which the 19th century is renowned. Visitors are welcome to inspect the engine and boilers and technical details are available. Overhead catwalks enable visitors to examine all parts. At the highest level adjacent to the huge iron beam are curious antiquities recovered from drains and land in the vicinity by engineers employed during the summer months maintaining the drains and dykes.

Originally rated at 60 h.p. the engine was uprated to 105 h.p. with a speed of 13-16 revolutions per minute. The scoopwheel is 2ft. 5ins. wide with a diameter of 37ft. 2ins. There are 48 ladles which lifted 30 tons of water with each revolution.

Ψ

The phenomenon of peat shrinkage was a well known fact in the era of wind engines. In the Isle of Ely about 230 wind-driven scoopwheels, when able, passed water from one to another in a comparatively relaxed manner. The area around Littleport including the West Norfolk Fens had no fewer than 75 wind engines which doubtlessly presented picturesque aspects to the beholder, but drainage was poor and in winter the fen became a vast lake. Even so, the engines had some effect and the peat fen began to shrink. This considerably accelerated with the advent of the steam pump. If anything it was too efficient and compelled drains to flow more vigorously, thereby extracting copious amounts of water from the peatland, similar to the effect of squeezing a sponge.

Efficiency through power of steam can be measured in the number of Watt-type beam engines which eventually replaced the sluggish wind-driven devices within the southern Fens. Nineteen steam units did the work of 250 wind engines. The steam engines were erected at Sutton St. Edmunds, Waldersea, North Brink near Wisbech, March West Fen, Binnimoor (March), White Fen, Mepal, Hundred Foot, Ten Mile Bank, Smithey Fen, Clear Fen, Swaffham Prior, Stretham, Little Thetford, Chettisham, Soham Mere, Prickwillow, Brandon (Feltwell), and Hilgay.

At Sutton St. Edmunds the Fens' first beam engine turned out a mere 12 h.p. draining in excess of 4,000 acres. Other engines were rated higher but even the lower rated machines made a dramatic impact on the land which several wind-engines could not achieve. The engine at Stretham replaced four such machines. At Littleport Fen when all 75 wind engines had been decommissioned a single 28 h.p. steamer performed the task. Another beam engine in the Isle of Ely was capable of lifting 40,000 gallons of water a minute.

Despite efficiency of power the outfalls, while considerably improved, continued to pose problems and some areas were likely to vanish beneath water. The beam engines operated well, but the water in the main drains built up rapidly, topped the banks and overflowed but flooding was not as serious and affected a smaller acreage. By that time so many embankments had been raised, if one was unable to contain the encroaching water another bank prevented the spillage from spreading to other areas.

Beam Engines: a few statistics

▷ Drainage of the Fens by steam first considered by the Commissioners of Middle Fen District in 1789.

▷ First beam engine of 12 h.p. installed at Sutton St. Edmund (North Level) in 1812 (annual operating cost £200).

▷ 30 h.p engine installed at Ten Mile Bank in 1820 (later uprated to 80 h.p.).

▷ 30 h.p. engine installed at Borough Fen (North Level) 1843.

▷ A 24 h.p. engine set up at Swaffham Fen in 1821. There was some argument as to whether a pump rather than the proven scoopwheel be employed. The latter was chosen, it being suggested that the operators liked them and were more familiar with maintenance.

▷ Two beam engines, 60 h.p. and 80 h.p. respectively began draining Deeping Fen in 1826.

▷ An 80 h.p. condensing beam engine erected at Hundred Foot Bank in 1829. This machine worked in conjunction with the engine at Ten Mile Bank.

▷ Stretham beam engine erected in 1831.

Falling cost of coal encouraged commissioners to rapidly install beam engines after 1832. This resulted in the abandonment of surviving wind engines. About 17 "steamers" were erected in the Lincolnshire Fens, and the Southern Fens (including the Isle of Ely) witnessed no fewer than 43 in action. The engines' scoopwheels could lift water from 6ft. to 20ft. Despite the changeover to steam being very costly it was, nonetheless, regarded as a revolutionary step towards the means of increasing agricultural production.

The only exception, the engine at Waldersea worked a bucket pump lifting 63 tons of water per minute. At March West Fen the engine lifted 70 tons per minute and earned itself special praise. S. Jonas in 1846 wrote that *"soon after its erection the lands were dry and splendid crops of corn grown the first year. I went over this land just after the flood and the lands were as dry as any in the country."* The scoopwheel had a diameter of 28ft. Relatively easy to maintain the traditional scoopwheel was by far the preferred method for use

Old Engine House : Stretham

T.A Bevis

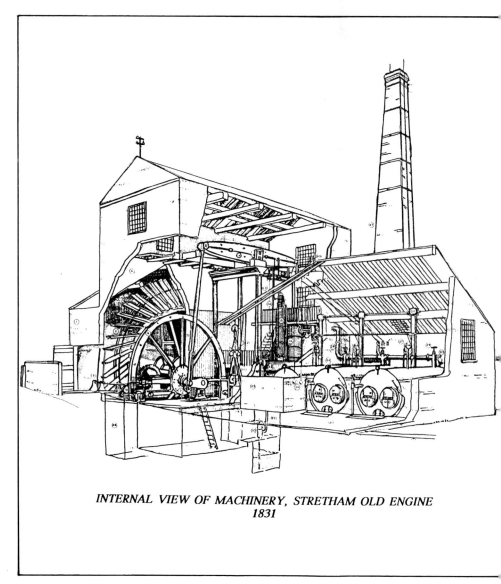

INTERNAL VIEW OF MACHINERY, STRETHAM OLD ENGINE
1831

Automatic electric pumps near Dog-in-a-Doublet Sluice.

(Photo. T. Bevis)

The sluice on the River Nene at Dog-in-a-Doublet, Whittlesey.　　*(Photo: T. Bevis)*

A huge water impeller powered by electricity. The Middle Level pumping station at Wiggenhall St. German's houses four impellers, two driven by diesel engines and two by electric motors. (Photo: T. Bevis)

One of the diesel engines added in recent years. It drives the water impeller enclosed in its casing in the background. (Photo: T. Bevis)

Looking down at an impeller and gear driven by one of the diesel engines; the flywheel is seen on the right. Each impeller is capable of discharging in excess of 1,300 tons of water per minute. **(Photo: T. Bevis)**

The massive survivor of three original diesel units at Wiggenhall St. Germans. Installed in 1934 this engine has eight horizontally opposed pistons, each weighing about half-a-ton. **(Photo: T. Bevis)**

in the Fens. The engines pumped astonishing amounts of water and levels were rapidly lowered. Largest scoopwheel was that fitted in 1881 to the Hundred Foot Bank engine. It had a diameter of 50ft., weighed 75 tons and scooped with sixty paddles.

Introduction of beam engines renewed confidence among the farming fraternity. The machines were the object of much curiosity among farmers, workers and casual visitors and it's a pity that almost all were scrapped at the end of their day. The three that do exist – at Stretham, Pinchbeck Marsh and near Boston are popular with steam buffs and those interested in land drainage. Long ago an observer had this to say about Fenland's steam pumps: *"To the minds of those living by the side of the rivers and drains of low, flat countries and accustomed to the slow practices of an agricultural life, there is a sense of power and solidity about a massive beam engine, with its slowly revolving flywheel and heavy beam, rising and falling, driving a ponderous waterwheel lifting a large mass of water."*

As with all innovations the efficient scoopwheel bowed to the inevitable. They were ponderous and heavy as were the engines that powered them, and they required extensive, lofty buildings altogether very costly to build. The machines were expensive to fuel and operate. Gradually the centrifugal pump replaced the scoopwheel. This was a clever device exhibited for the first time at the Great Exhibition. It attracted much interest and it is not surprising that the machine – the Apold – was employed to drain Whittlesey Mere, culminating in outstanding success thus assuring it of a successful future.

The new pumping system was noticeably efficient but it accelerated land shrinkage to an all time record. The effect upon crop production and profits was phenomenal as were also the costs of countering land shrinkage. The peat soil depleted progressvely over a period of 200 years of intensive drainage and farming. In some places clay is raised with ploughing and it is not inconceivable that in the next generation or so large areas of the Fens will have been exhausted and take on the aspect of "pastures for Essex calves." Another assumption, not without good reason it would seem, the so-called greenhouse effect said to be raising the sea level, could cause the Fens to become a vast inland lake, an extension of the Wash possibly, creating an environment of seals rather than eels. A huge system of defensive sea barriers would have to be built to prevent this from happening. That, however, is for the future to decide.

At the beginning of the First World War the Bedford Level Corporation was replaced by a number of drainage boards, the members mostly from the farming community. In 1930 an Act of Parliament placed the entire Bedford Level under the auspices of the Ouse Catchment Board with increased responsibilities maintaining the sluices, natural rivers and artificial drains. Helpful degrees of co-operation exists between the Government and the Board, the former recognising the importance of such a large and vulnerable agricultural and horticultural area. Arguably the lowest agricultural area in the country, the Fens are unique; some areas, i.e. in the vicinity of March, lie practically at sea level. Vigilence is constantly necessary as regards the age-old battle against water which, were it not for a highly sophisticated drainage system integrated at all authoritative levels would all too easily reclaim its old domain.

Situated at strategic sites, the new generation of Fen guardians – dozens of diesel and electric powered pumps of varying capacities, manned and automatic, wait at a high state of readiness. To hear the steady, rhythmic throbbing of a set of powerful diesel engines driving impellers in low-profile buildings crouched above main drains is reassuring music to the inhabitants of Fenland. The units somehow epitomise the problems experienced by Fenmen of old when the farmer went out to sow and harvested eels instead!

The Fens' first diesel pump was installed in Methwold and Feltwell district in 1913. It had to cope with a lift of 6ft. attributable to land shrinkage over the course of half a century. Constant readjustment was necessary and a second pumping station had to be built. Raising water to discharge levels has long been a problem in the Fens. In the South and North Levels lifts of 21ft. were known. Nowadays it is very important to lower the amount of discharge in order to retain sufficient water in the land, a requirement magnified by less than normal rainfall and unusually hot summers recurring from 1989. Several pumps start automatically when the water level rises and cut off when it recedes to the appropriate level. In some places it was necessary to reduce discharge from outlets of 42ins. (150 tons per minute) to 24ins. (70 tons per minute).

Diesel and electric pumps have obvious advantages not the least superb efficiency. Compared with huge steam pumps which stood on heavy foundations excavated in light soil, diesel units require less substantial footings. When steaming intermittently the old beam engines had to be prepared and primed and delay was inevitable until the engine was brought into a good head of steam. The fire had to be raked out until the engine was needed again necessitating heavy fuel consumption. Modern diesel and electric units start instantly and are highly satisfactory for intermittent pumping. Ample stocks of fuel are conveniently on tap to engines and electricity available at the touch of a button.

The advantage of diesel power was not, at first, popular. In the second decade of the century Europe was involved in war and a veil of despondency hung above the country. This had a noticeable effect on the farming fraternity. However, postwar years witnessed a revival in land drainage improvements and diesel engines rapidly replaced out-dated machinery. In the nineteen-thirties there was almost total conversion to efficient, cheaply-run diesel systems. The Fens are recognised as a prime area of food production, particularly in time of war. The Government supported drainage improvement schemes and, with the threat of the Second World War looming, there was an urgency to install modern pumping plants.

During World War Two sixty-two pumping stations costing in excess of £400,000 were erected in the Fens. Plants such as that at Tydd Gote (North Level) which can pump more than 10 million gallons per hour, and Bevills Leam pumping station (Middle Level) capable of discharging 1,080 tons per minute evoke deserved interest. But it is at Wiggenhall St. Germans that Europe's largest land drainage pumps crouch above the Middle Level Main Drain. The machinery staggers the mind with statistics. The pumping station was constructed between 1930 and 1934 and stands upon concrete foundations supported by 1,245 reinforced concrete piles. This famous drainage complex was built with the aid of a special grant conditional upon seventy-five per cent of the labour force being recruited from the country's distressed areas.

Originally three diesels were installed but due to a decline in the gravity drainage a fourth diesel engine and impeller was added in 1951. In full cry the four huge units are capable of lifting 6,000,000 tons of water with twenty-four hours continuous pumping. It is an education to stand on the "bridge" outside and watch the gush of frothing water discharging via double entry centrifugal pumps into the River Ouse. Some modification has taken place since 1951, units in the north engine house replaced by two electric motors of 1,550 h.p. at 985 revolutions per minute (pump rotational speed 98 r.p.m.). The south engine house retains two diesel units, one eight cylinder VAV of 1,500 h.p. (215 r.p.m.) installed in 1951. Its companion has eight cylinders (18½in. bore) turbo charged 1,550 h.p at 1,000 r.p.m. (modified 1982/83). Pumps in this building have rotational speeds of 95 and 98 r.p.m. respectively. From 1983 the total capacity of water discharged amounted to 4,260 tons per minute.

The pumps at St. Germans are seldom used in summer months. In the winter of 1943/44 they clocked up only 51 pumping hours. It is in extreme winters like that of 1947 that the Guardians vent their anger. That year proved a disaster to the Fens, severe flooding occurring in areas adjacent to the River Great Ouse and the River Welland, near Crowland where army vehicles were used to plug breached embankments. In the spring of that year St. Germans pumping station recorded 647 hours pumping in a single spell. In another period of eleven months with above average rainfall the pumps laboured 3,800 hours. Since 1934 more than a hundred new pumping stations were constructed by minor Boards covering the Middle Level area and since 1940 the total pumping capacity in this, the largest of the three Levels has increased by around fifty per cent.

The Middle Level covers an extensive area shaped roughly like a triangle stretching from beyond the new Catchwater Drain west of Ramsey, northwards to Wiggenhall in Norfolk; and from Whittlesey and March to the north bank of the Old Bedford river. Discharge is via a network of dykes, rivers and drains from a water level practically equal to that of the land. On several occasions the pumps at St. Germans, backed by numerous smaller units in the Middle Level area saved the rich farmland from inundation. There is no better drainage system in the country. Without it the Fens would be drowned and March and other places revert to islands again.

From 1970 onwards low water levels in the area revived the old spectre of land shrinkage. This is particularly noticeable in the south west of the Middle Level where the gradient has entirely gone. To grapple with this phenomenon the Middle Level Major Improvement Scheme was devised and work continued from 1977 to 1983. It includes a Booster Station at Tebbitts Bridge on Bevills Leam working with the downstream drainage system by regulating flows from the upland brooks between Ramsey, Peterborough and the A1 motorway.

The pumping station contains six axial flow pumps, three powered by electricity and three run by diesel units. The total discharge capacity amounts to 1,080 tons per minute, about a quarter of the water discharged at full capacity at St. Germans. A catchwater drain was cut along the edge of the upland and involved the removal of 450,000 cubic meters of material and the provision of twelve vehicular bridges. At the same time the Nature Reserve at Woodwalton was borne in mind and provision made for the storage of 1.8 million cubic meters of water. The scheme became operable in 1983 after the completion of an isolating lock on the River Nene (old course) at Lodes End, near Ramsey.

$$\psi$$

The inundation of 1947 illustrated that the battle against flooding had by no means been won. It was a winter of above average snowfall with hard frosts and deluges of rain. The rain could not penetrate frozen snow and the problem was compounded by frozen dykes and drains. When thaw eventually started heavy rain added to the surface water; rivers were excessively burdened and drifting ice hampered pumping stations. The author recalls to mind drowned animals held by the underpart of Guyhirn's old bridge, poles being used to release them. Water spread out into the Fens and invaded river valleys. At one place it rose eight feet in four days and the sluice at Dog-in-a-Doublet on the River Nene remained raised for thirty-one days. The amount of water swiftly passing beneath the gates was unbelievable. At Wansford gauge station west of Peterborough on March 8th the flow registered 285 million gallons per hour.

These post-war floods proved that men's sophisiticated drainage systems were not infallible, and however efficient there can be no guarantee that such things will not happen again. Nature bides her time and with awesome majesty strikes at her chosen hour. It is a lesson which Vuymuyden and successive engineers recognised: men can improve on the past but never must they cease to be vigilant.

In 1638 Vermuyden built the original sluice at Denver but it collapsed in 1713 to the undisguised delight of some who hoped the Fens would revert to its former watery state. The sluice had not really improved anything; rather it worsened the situation by restricting the time for the fresh water in the Bedford rivers to escape between tides. As a result silt built up in the Ouse between Denver and the outfall. The last six miles was notoriously bad, the river restricted by silt beds over a four-mile bend (see illustration). It was forty years before another sluice was built, and the farmers and other Fen inhabitants turned severely against the Bedford Level Corporation who had also to contend with attitudes of King's Lynn Corporation, ever suspicious of "improvements" likely to disrupt navigation.

Successive sluices erected at Denver operated with mixed fortunes and it was not until John Rennie, versatile engineer, had turned his attention to the matter that the river flow improved. As early as 1789 Rennie – designer of bridges, canals, lighthouses and breakwaters – was attracted to the drowned state of low lying land near Ely. He recommended the application of Watt's steam engine to pump water away from Botteshaw and Soham Fens, an area of 5,000 acres known as Rotten Land. Loath to change, the Fenmen would have nothing to do with this suggestion, preferring unreliable wind engines instead. Later, Rennie proved his worth by effectively draining in 1807 large areas of fen in south Lincolnshire. It had long been realised that a by-pass to eliminate the notorious curve on the River Ouse near King's Lynn would solve some problems arising from silting. Accordingly Rennie was appointed chief engineer of the Eau Bank project at Lynn, and he designed a straight cut making the former hazardous water course redundant. Work on this project started in 1817 and such was the improvement to flow and navigation Rennie was accorded the highest accolade that Fenmen could give: "Slayer of dragons!"

After the disaster of 1947 a Flood Protection Scheme was conceived and work on this carried out between 1954-64 at a cost of £10,400,000. A similar scheme had been devised by Vermuyden 316 years anterior to that time. His plan was to provide a relief channel beginning at a point west of Mildenhall and terminating just above King's Lynn. It did not materialise. The modern cut-off channel, almost 29 miles long, served by sluices begins at Barton Mills and enters the River Ouse a few miles from King's Lynn. The channel skirts the edge of the Fens near the rivers Wissey, Little Ouse and Lark. Since its completion, as yet no floods have occurred except by controllable incursion onto the picturesque washland between the Old and New Bedford rivers, internationally renowned nature reserves, and on washland between Guyhirn and Whittlesey.

Another modern problem is that of erosion, water eating steadily at the lower part of embankments. In some cases piling is used to protect these vulnerable areas and the laying down of gravel, too, helps to protect the banks. Fenland with its hundreds of miles of waterways and new marinas is becoming increasingly popular with river tourists and this can have a detrimental effect on river banks which adds to the cost of maintaining the complex system utilised in extensive land drainage. The battle goes on. In seven centuries of land reclamation in the historical Fens, fortune and misfortune variously attended the efforts of man to conquer the rampaging frolics of freshwater and sea. Only time will tell whether at long last he has wrested final victory from his relentless, timeless foe.

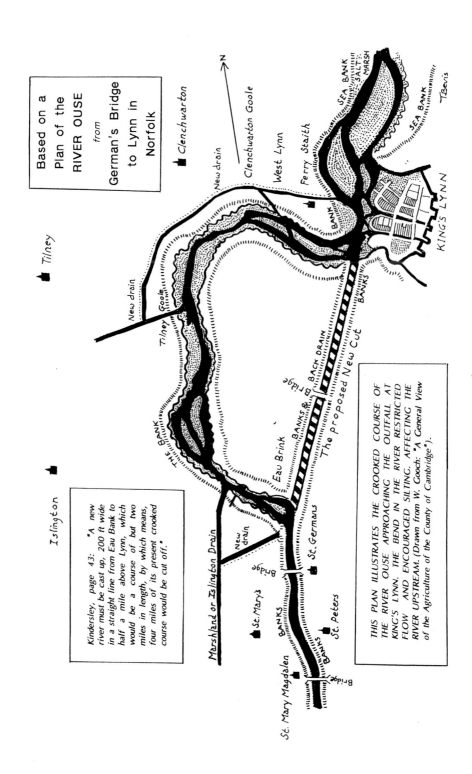

Based on a
Plan of the
RIVER OUSE

from

German's Bridge
to Lynn in
Norfolk

Kindersley, page 43: "A new
river must be cast up, 200 ft wide
in a straight line from Eau Bank to
half a mile above Lynn, which
would be a course of but two
miles in length, by which means,
four miles of its present crooked
course would be cut off."

THIS PLAN ILLUSTRATES THE CROOKED COURSE OF
THE RIVER OUSE APPROACHING THE OUTFALL AT
KING'S LYNN. THE BEND IN THE RIVER RESTRICTED
FLOW AND ENCOURAGED SILTING, AFFECTING THE
RIVER UPSTREAM. (Drawn from W. Gooch: "A General View
of the Agriculture of the County of Cambridge").

N

Tilney

Islington

Clenchwarton

Clenchwarton Goole

West Lynn

Ferry Staith

KING'S LYNN

SEA BANK

SALT MARSH

SEA BANK

Bevis

BANK

THE BANK

New drain

Tilney Goole

New drain

The proposed New Cut

BANKS

Eau Brink

BANKS & BRIDGE

BACK DRAIN

Bridge

St. Germans

St. Marys

New drain

Marshland or Islington Drain

St. Peters

BANKS

St. Mary Magdalen

BANKS

Bridge

CHAPTER SIX

The "ruinous state of Manea"

AN ILLUSTRATION of the calamitous effects which drainage had on some Fen parishes in the 18th century is seen from that which affected Manea. It seems ironic that this parish declined from a position of wealth and well being to one fallen upon hard times. Had Charles the First lived, it was planned that the village be redeveloped to a position of dignity among the possessions of the ill-fated royal.

Situated in the midst of the King's 12,000 acres of former wet Fen, Manea, according to Dugdale was destined to be a place of paradise. The King, he wrote, intended "to enrich the Fens by several plantations and diverse ample privileges." Among these was his ambition to build an eminent town in the middle of the great Level at the village of Manea and have it renamed Charlemont. He drew up a plan of his Fen estate which included a navigable stream from Manea to the River Great Ouse. He designed a large house overlooking the village and it is significant that there existed at Manea an artificial square mound which it is supposed was thrown up on the King's orders. Manea was to be the centrepiece in the plan to regenerate the royal coffers from abundant wealth squeezed from the Fens. This earned Cromwell's initial hostility to the drainage scheme.

As it turned out Charles was executed and Cromwell, the Lord Protector, supported the scheme, which included the installation of numerous wind engines in the area. These were an attributable cause to Manea's unforeseeable decline. The engines threw prodigious amounts of water upon the parish which by reason of its geological situation it could not reject. Another cause was a large tunnel laid down in 1712 passing beneath the Forty Foot river to defend the lower areas of the Middle Level from water excluded from the upper parts. Along this tunnel water poured from a large area of land into the Sixteen Foot river, the only drain Manea had to carry off its water. On occasions the overburdened river overflowed into the dykes and Manea was drowned. A third cause was the deterioration of the River Great Ouse outfall after the collapse of Denver Sluice in 1713.

Of the wind engines a traveller wrote in his diary: *"There are no less than 250 in the Middle Level. In Whittlesey parish only, I was told by some of the principal inhabitants there were more than fifty mills, and there are as many in Doddington Parish (including March and Benwick). I myself riding from Ramsey to Holme, about six miles, counted forty in my view. These are between Ramsey and Old Bedford bank, and upon the Forty Foot and Twenty Foot, and to Salter's Lode in Welle parish (surrounding Manea) fifty-seven. "*

Prior to these "improvements" the parish of Manea could reckon to be inundated in winter with about two feet of water. The floods usually occurred through a breach in the river bank but the water had drained away before summer and farmers harvested good crops from the land. Then along came the engineers and others and set up scores of windmills the effect on Manea being to reduce the flood waters to twelve inches, but unlike old times it just would not drain away and the land could hardly be got dry all summer. Whilst most farmers in the Fens thrived, those at Manea were reduced almost to beggary. From being called rich Manea the parish was said to be the poorest in the land.

The Wash between Mepal and Welney.

Addendum
EARLY WIND ENGINES

After the embanking of the Waldersea and Coldham Ring, an area enclosing Keeke's Mill, Ring's End, Hobbs House, Elm Leam, Redmore Dyke and Begdale, Mr. Carlton, governor of Wisbech castle and owner of land within The Ring, in 1580 erected a few wind engines introduced to England by Peter Morris, a Dutchman. That year appears to be the earliest reference to wind engines in the Fens. Other devices were on the market. Sir Thomas Golding of Powles Sellchamp, Essex, held a licence to use a wind engine which served as a watermill, a cornmill and a water works to carry water into the town.

Fenmen hated the machines which they called "Gewgaws," and viewed them with justified trepidation. Carlton found it difficult to hire labourers to erect the engines and keep them working. To Fenmen the new-fangled devices presaged the time when the Fens would be devoid of water and inhabitants rendered redundant. Petitions against the machines were numerous yet many were erected and eventually the drainage authorities were obliged to order that privately owned engines, such as that at Green's Mill (1699) near Chatteris, be demolished.

PRICKWILLOW DRAINAGE ENGINE MUSEUM

This building originally contained a steam engine and pump. The main exhibit is a Mirrlees, Bickerton and Day diesel engine of 259 h.p. driving a 42 inch centrifugal pump discharging 140 tons of water per minute. It was opened in July 1923. The engine clocked up about 44,000 hours of pumping before being retired. Other "rescued" engines are a Vickers Petter, Ruston, Allen, and Listers all arranged around the main engine. These engines all served the Fenland drainage system at various pumping stations in the area. They are of varying capacities and impressively engineered. The building dates to 1880 and the steam engine it contained worked at 38 r.p.m.

Also displayed are old tools and implements familiar to the Fens with old photographs associated with the area's long history of land drainage. It is sobering to realise that the level of the Fen in the vicinity has dropped to its present level of about four feet below mean sea level and how easy it would transform to a morass again were it not for the modern system of drainage supported by the new generation of diesel and electric pumps. The museum exhibits have been painstakingly re-assembled and restored by a dedicated team of volunteers. Special "Run Days" are organised - usually on a Sunday - at certain times of the year in aid of the Engine Trust. It is usually possible to run the main engine for groups by prior arrangement.

With the beam engine at Stretham being restored in the winter of 1992-93 and plans to enlarge the Prickwillow Drainage Engine Museum in hand, it is pleasing that here in the Fens where anciently water reigned supreme, the old engines of earlier generations are being preserved so well for the gratification of all that admire the quality and durability with which those ages of English engineering skill are renowned.

Stretham and Prickwillow engine houses are uniquely placed to demonstrate the history and ecology of the drained Fenlands of East Anglia and no less a tribute to the expertise of the past engineers. Both establishments, one embracing the nostalgic age of steam power, the other the economical advances of diesel power are valuable resources for education and leisure representing important aspects of our heritage in engineering, agriculture and rural life. They epitomise the endeavour, disappointment and achievement experienced by the earlier drainage experts, transcended by revolutionary techniques which, seen in these buildings, were giant steps from the age of the elegant and gentle wind engines which dotted the Fenland landscape.

Addendum

ST. GERMAN'S PUMPING STATION

Plans were made in 1929 to recruit a large number of workless men from distressed areas and employ them on the site of the new pumping station, the largest of its kind in Europe. They were obliged to accept certain conditions, one being that every man must come clean in person and have at least one change of underclothing. The labourers were paid 9d. per hour (36s. for a 48 hour week), but deductions were made for Unemployment and Health Stamp. Catering was on communal lines and cost each man 10s. a week. A cook was provided and every man had to bring a knife, fork and spoon.

Coming from considerable distances workers were accommodated in specially built huts (28 to a hut, four to a cubicle). Beds, blankets, fire and light were provided free as were cooking utensils issued to each man. It was expected of everyone to take a hot bath once a week. The Middle Level Drainage and Navigational Board "went to considerable expense providing facilities for hot baths. It is found from experience that unless something of this nature is done the camp bedding, etc. is liable to become unclean." Men conducting themselves in a manner to jeopardize the health and comfort of others were discharged.

Casting of hundreds of concrete piles began on February 19th, 1930. The first batch were between 30ft. and 47ft. long with a total lineal footage of 29,322. There were 908 reinforced concrete piles and 808 steel sheet piles – between 22ft. and 40ft. long (a total of 22,283 lineal feet). Steel sheet was driven over a distance of 1,060 feet. 1,236 cubic yards of mass concrete fifteen feet thick formed the foundations underpinned by 1,245 piles to withstand the massive pounding of the three original diesel units each driving a huge, encased impeller.

There was modest pumping activity during the droughts of 1990 and 1991 and into 1992, as much water as possible being conserved for the use of irrigation in the Fens. Each unit is worked occasionally, a necessary precaution especially in the case of the two remaining diesel units to keep them in prime working order. Movement of water by use of pumping action is generally a good thing. Some rivers in the Fens are linked to modern sewage disposal plants which discharge clean but "dead" water into the system. Causing rivers to flow helps to oxygenate them.

EXTRACTS FROM VERMUYDEN'S DISCOURSE ON DRAINAGE, 1642

"*The Level lieth in six Counties: Cambridge and the Isle of Ely, Huntingdon, Northampton, Lincoln, Norfolk and Suffolk. It is of vast and great extent . . . There doe run through these fenns eight rivers, Glean, Welland, Neane, Ouse, Grant, Mildenhall, Brandon and Stoke. The said rivers have three several outfalls from the fennes into the sea, and by these outfalls the said rivers and lands unwater themselves in that manner as now they doe . . .*

"*The Level is broad, and of great extent and flat with little or no descent of its own, and grown full of hassocks, sedge and reed, and the rivers full of weeds; and the waters go slowly away from the lands and out of the rivers, and they come swift into it and upon it out of the Upland Counties where the rivers have a great fall . . . The tydes every day bring into the mouth of the rivers a great quantity (sand) thereof and there is but a few times sufficient land water to set the sands out again to keep the outfall open, insomuch that Welland and Wisbich outfalls are choked every summer; but the outfall of Lynn hath sufficient water to keep open his channel, and although in summer the sands in Lynn haven overcome the ebbs somewhat yet they do not lie long, but the first land waters of next spring tydes carry them away again.*

"*But it is not only to be feared, but apparent, that in process of time, the outfalls of Wisbich and Welland will utterly decay by the said increase and sands of the sea, if they should remain as now they are by reason of the daily increase of the marshes.*

"*The soyl of this vast country is moorish, gathered and grown up higher by the weeds and ooze of the waters; many of them are rich grounds, and all would (if they were well drained) be very profitable and become good grounds especially after they be burned, manured and husbanded as such grounds should be.*

"*There be many isles and rising grounds within this great level, and the rivers pass by towns low seated, lying here or next unto the Uplands, wherein the inhabitants of the fennes doe live in great aboundance. The said countries of Marshland, Wisbich and Holland are fenced by banks from the waters of the fennes, and sometimes they have been overflown by the said waters and have often been in great danger, and they are at continual charge for the maintenance of the said banks. The King's contract is to make these lands winter ground, that is to free them from the overflowing of the rivers aforesaid, as far by art can be devised.*"

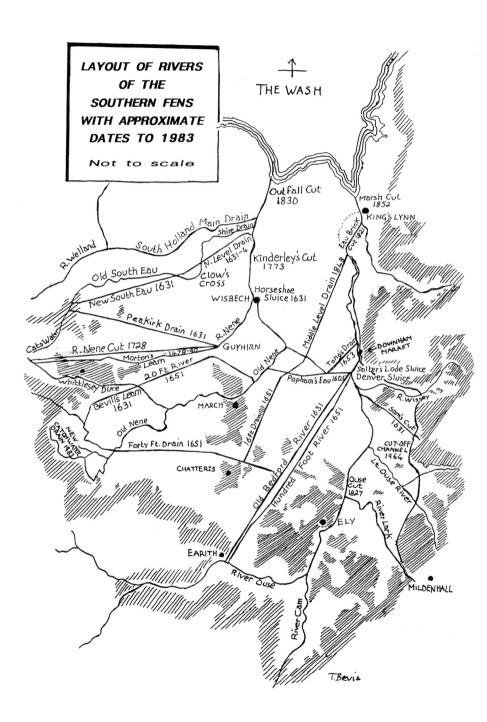

LAYOUT OF RIVERS
OF THE
SOUTHERN FENS
WITH APPROXIMATE
DATES TO 1983

Not to scale

THE WASH

Outfall Cut
1830

Marsh Cut
1852

KING'S LYNN

South Holland Main Drain

Shire Drain

R. Welland

Old South Eau

N. Level Drain
1631-4

Clow's
Cross

Kinderley's Cut
1773

Eau Brink Cut 1821

New South Eau 1631

Horseshoe
Sluice 1631

WISBECH

Middle Level Drain 1848

Peakirk Drain 1631

R. Nene

DOWNHAM
MARKET

Cats Water

R. Nene Cut 1728

Morton's
Leam   1478-90

GUYHIRN

Tong's Drain
1653

Old Nene

Salter's Lode Sluice
Denver Sluice

Whittlesey Dike

20 Ft. River
1651

Popham's Eau 1605

R. Wissey

Bevill's Leam
1631

MARCH

16 Ft. Drain 1651

Sam's Cut
1631

NEW CATCHWATER DRAIN 1982

Old Nene

Forty Ft. Drain 1651

CUT-OFF
CHANNEL
1964

CHATTERIS

Old Bedford River 1651

Hundred Foot River 1651

Ouse
Cut
1827

Lt. Ouse River

ELY

River Lark

EARITH

River Ouse

MILDENHALL

River Cam

T. Bevis